Fly through Reception Phonics with CGP!

CGP's Targeted Practice Books are packed with fun and friendly activities to build Reception pupils' confidence as they start to read and write.

What's more, they follow the National Curriculum 'Letters and Sounds' programme, so you can be sure they cover everything children need to learn.

This is **Reception Targeted Practice Book 2**. It covers the second part of **Phase 2** of the 'Letters and Sounds' programme, including:

- The letters **g**, **o**, **c**, **k**, **e**, **u**, **r**, **h**, **b**, **f** and **l**
- Plus some **double letters** and **tricky words**

What CGP is all about

Our sole aim here at CGP is to produce the highest quality books
— carefully written, immaculately presented and
dangerously close to being funny.

Then we work our socks off to get them out to you
— at the cheapest possible prices.

How to Use this Book

In this Book

You'll meet...

 **Letter Lizards**: they'll help you write letters and learn about letter sounds

 **Jolly Jugglers**: they'll help you practise those tricky words

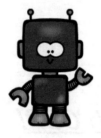 **Friendly Robots**: they'll help you speak in robot-talk

 Word Birds: they'll help you blend sounds to read words

Hints for Helpers

Here are a few things to bear in mind when using this book:

- CGP's Phonics series aligns with **Letters and Sounds**, the Department for Education's systematic synthetic phonics programme. Book 1 introduced content from the early part of Phase 2. This book continues and completes the Phase 2 content.

- The book should be worked through **in order**, as new content builds on content covered earlier in the book.

- **'Robot-talk'** in this book is equivalent to **'sound-talk'** in Letters and Sounds. It refers to breaking down a word into its individual sounds. For example, the word **coat** has three separate sounds: **c - oa - t**.

- A **'word frame'** in this book is equivalent to a **'phoneme frame'** in Letters and Sounds. It is used to help with spelling. The frame has one box for each sound.

- Letters that are shown in inverted commas should always be said as **letter sounds**, **not letter names**. Avoid adding extra sounds (for **"s"**, say **'sss'** not **'suh'**).

- This resource requires children to match images to words. You may need to help children to **identify** some images they're not sure of.

> Above all, promote a **positive, confident attitude** towards reading and writing by giving lots of praise and encouragement.

Contents

Written by Karen Bryant-Mole

Editors: Laura Collins, Christopher Lindle, Sam Mann, Sam Norman, Hannah Roscoe
Reviewers: Ross Knaggs, Clare Leck, Lucy Towle
With thanks to Sharon Gulliver, Anne James and Holly Robinson for the proofreading.
ISBN: 978 1 78908 012 4

Clipart from Corel®
Images throughout the book from www.edu-clips.com
Printed by Elanders Ltd, Newcastle upon Tyne.
Based on the classic CGP style created by Richard Parsons.

Book 1 Check

Say what you see. Two words start with the same sound.
One starts with a different sound. **Colour** the odd one out.

Say each letter sound.
Match each letter to something that starts with that sound.

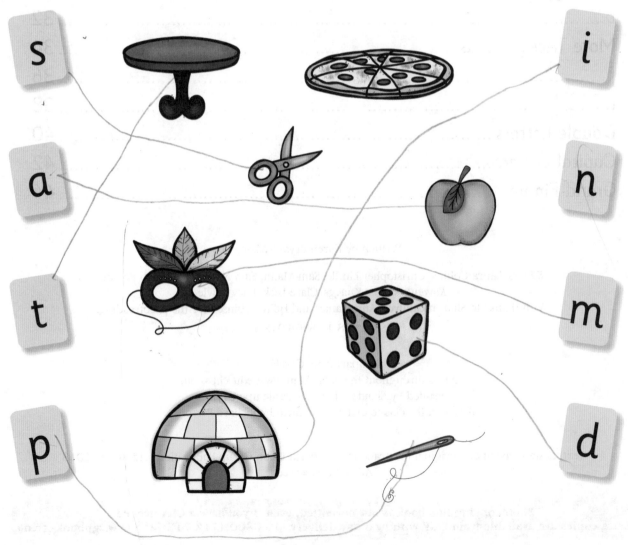

Say what you see. **Say** the sound the word starts with.
Circle the letter for that sound.

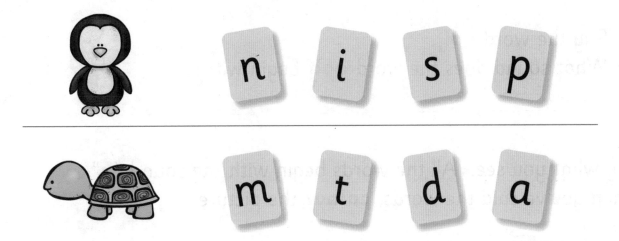

n   i   s   p

m   t   d   a

Read the captions under each picture. **Circle** the correct caption.

| tin | pan | sad |
| tip | man | pad |

Match each letter in the top row to its capital letter below.

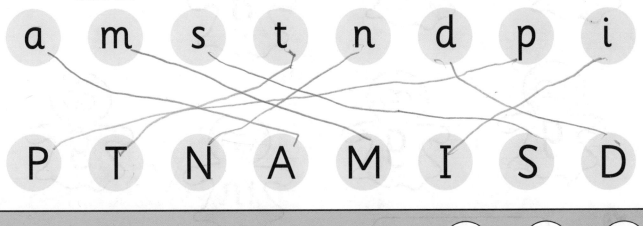

a   m   s   t   n   d   p   i

P   T   N   A   M   I   S   D

I can remember everything I learned in Book 1.

Phonics — Reception Book 2

g

Say the word golf.
What sound does the word golf begin with?

Say what you see. All the words begin with the sound "g".
When you've said the words, **colour** the pictures.

This is the letter for the sound "g".
Find all the ghosts with this letter. **Circle** them.

What sound do you hear
at the start of ghost?

Trace over the grey letter with your finger.
Write over the dotted letters, then **write** some letters by yourself.

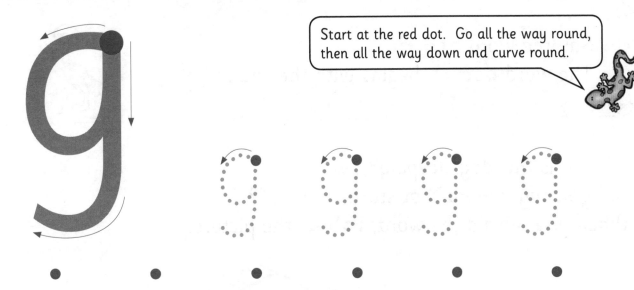

Start at the red dot. Go all the way round, then all the way down and curve round.

Look at the letter in the frame below. **Say** the sound.
Put a **tick** (✓) below the objects that start with this sound.

I can hear the sound "g". I can recognise and write the letter for the sound "g".

Phonics — Reception Book 2

o

Say the word **ostrich**.
The word **ostrich** begins with the sound "**o**".

Where is this dog sleeping?
Did you say a word that starts with "**o**"?
When you've said the word, **colour** the picture.

This is the letter for the sound "**o**".
Find all the octagons with this letter. **Circle** them.

g

o

o

o

n

o

o

i

Say the sound you hear
at the start of octagon.

Trace over the grey letter with your finger.
Write over the dotted letters, then write some letters by yourself.

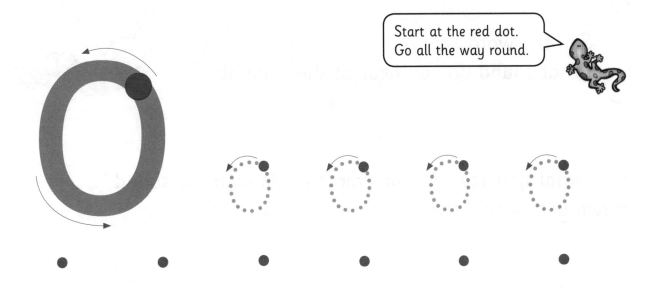

Start at the red dot.
Go all the way round.

Look at the letter in the frame below. Say the sound.
Put a tick (✓) below the objects that start with this sound.

I can hear the sound "o". I can recognise
and write the letter for the sound "o".

c

Say the word **caterpillar**.
What sound do you hear at the beginning?

Say what you see. All the words begin with the sound "**c**".
When you've said the words, **colour** the pictures.

This is the letter for the sound "**c**".
Find all the clouds with this letter. **Circle** them.

What sound does the
word **cloud** start with?

Trace over the grey letter with your finger.
Write over the dotted letters, then write some letters by yourself.

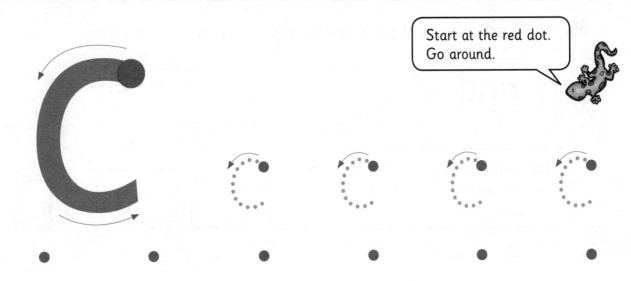

Start at the red dot.
Go around.

Look at the letter in the frame below. Say the sound.
Put a tick (✓) below the objects that start with this sound.

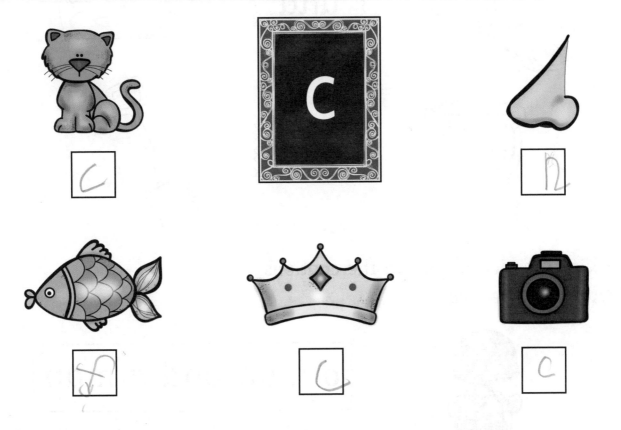

I can hear the sound "c". I can recognise
and write the letter for the sound "c".

Phonics — Reception Book 2

Captions with 'and'

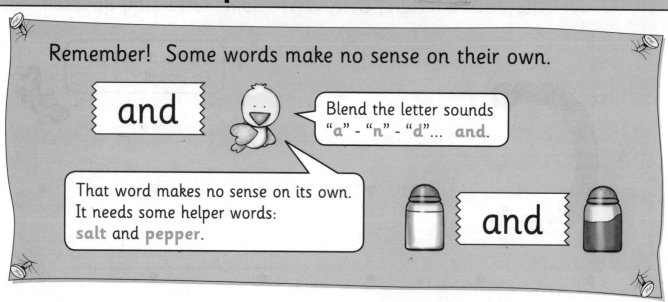

Remember! Some words make no sense on their own.

and

Blend the letter sounds "a" - "n" - "d"... and.

That word makes no sense on its own. It needs some helper words: salt and pepper.

and

Say the words for the pictures and **read** the captions.
Colour the pictures.

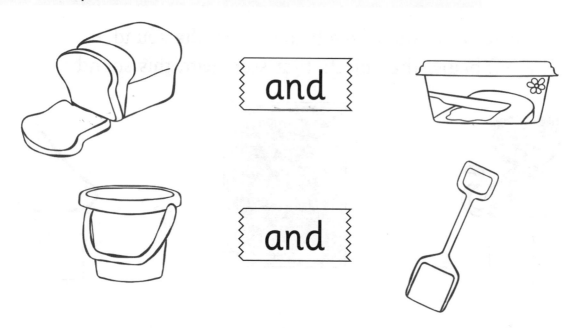

and

and

Look at the picture. **Read** the captions.
Circle the correct caption.

a man and a map

a man and a mop

Read the captions. **Colour** the pictures.

That's clever! If you put the letter for the sound "s" at the end of **tin**, it makes the word **tins**.

| tin | tins |

Read each caption. **Match** it to the correct picture.

| pots and pans |

| pins and a pad |

Read the caption. **Draw** a picture to go with the caption.

| cats and dogs |

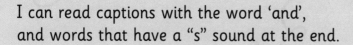

I can read captions with the word 'and', and words that have a "s" sound at the end.

k

Say the word koala.
Say the sound the word koala begins with.

Say what you see. All the words begin with the sound "k".
When you've said the words, colour the pictures.

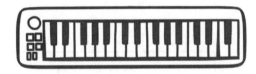

This is the **letter** for the sound "k".
Find all the kites with this letter. **Circle** them.

Kite starts with the same sound as caterpillar but this time the sound has a different letter.

Trace over the grey letter with your finger.
Write over the dotted letters, then write some letters by yourself.

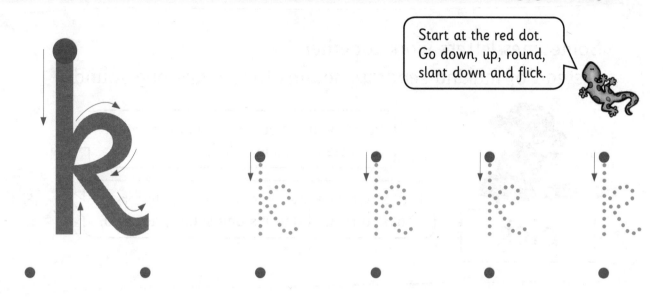

Start at the red dot.
Go down, up, round,
slant down and flick.

Look at the letter in the frame below. Say the sound.
Put a tick (✓) below the objects that start with this sound.

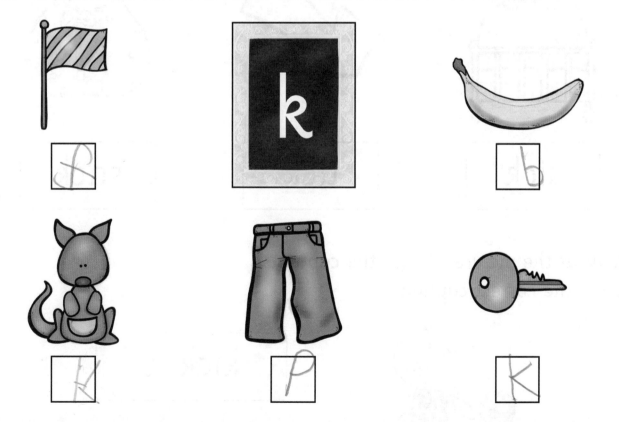

I can hear the sound "k". I can recognise
and write the letter for the sound "k".

Phonics — Reception Book 2

Words with -ck

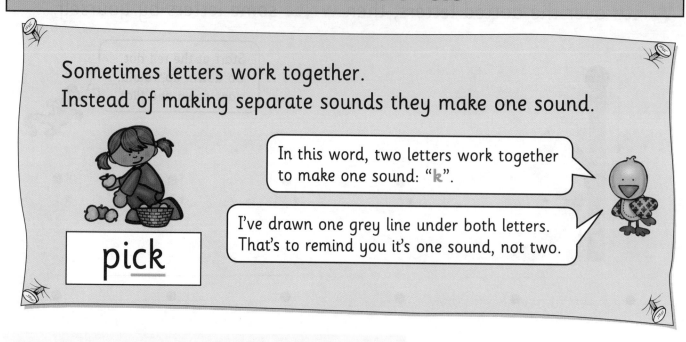

Sometimes letters work together.
Instead of making separate sounds they make one sound.

In this word, two letters work together to make one sound: "**k**".

I've drawn one grey line under both letters. That's to remind you it's one sound, not two.

pick

Read the captions. **Colour** the pictures.

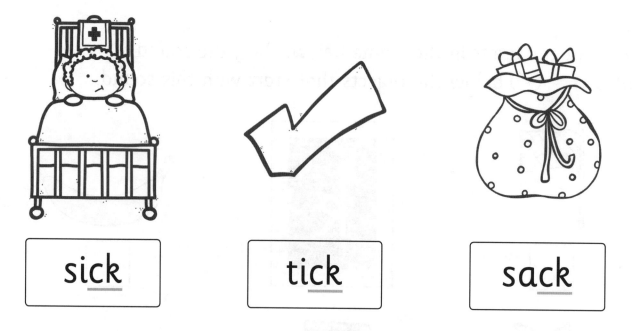

sick

tick

sack

Look at the picture. **Read** the captions.
Circle the correct caption.

kick it

pack it

Read the caption. Colour the pictures.

tick tock

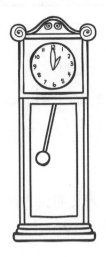

These words actually sound like the noise a clock makes! Can you think of a word that sounds like the noise a bee makes?

Read each caption. Match it to the correct picture.

Nick sits

Mack digs

Read the caption. Draw a picture to go with the caption.

dots on a sock

I know that letters sometimes work together to make one sound. I know that -ck makes a "k" sound.

Phonics — Reception Book 2

e

Say the word empty.
Do you hear the sound "e" at the beginning?

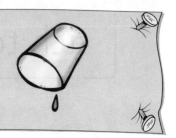

Say what you see. All the words begin with the sound "e".
When you've said the words, colour the pictures.

You'll need to think hard about these!

This is the letter for the sound "e".
Find all the envelopes with this letter. Circle them.

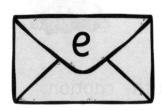

I say envelope with an "e" sound at the start. Do you?

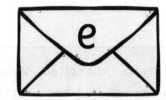

Phonics — Reception Book 2

Trace over the grey letter with your finger.
Write over the dotted letters, then write some letters by yourself.

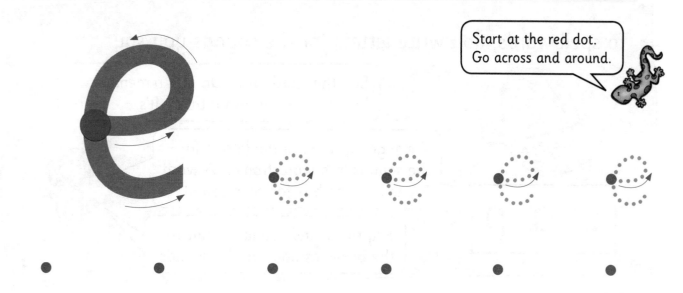

Start at the red dot.
Go across and around.

Look at the letter in the frame below. Say the sound.
Put a tick (✓) below the objects that start with this sound.

I can hear the sound "e". I can recognise
and write the letter for the sound "e".

Phonics — Reception Book 2

Starting to Spell

To spell words, you write letters for the sounds you say.

Say the word **cap**. Do you remember how to say it in robot-talk? It's **c - a - p**.

We're going to write the letters for the sounds in a word frame. A word frame has one box for each sound.

Say the sounds again. Point to the boxes as you say the sounds.

Say the word **pan** in robot-talk.
How many sounds are there? **Circle** the correct picture.

Say the words **tag**, **mop** and **pad** in robot-talk.
Point to the boxes in the word frames as you say the sounds.
Copy the letters into the empty word frames.

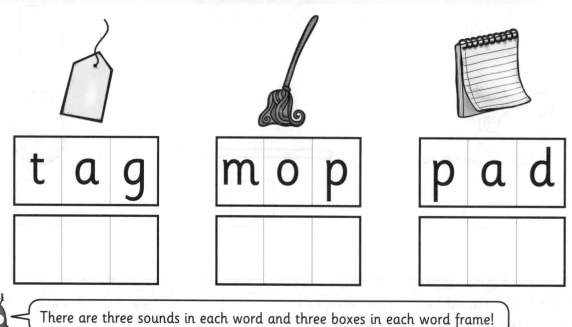

There are three sounds in each word and three boxes in each word frame!

Say the words **mat**, **dog** and **pin** in robot-talk.
There's a letter missing from the end of each word.
Complete the words in the word frames below.

These letter cards will help you.
Find the card for the missing sound.
Copy the letter into the word frame.

Say the words **cat**, **tap** and **pen** in robot-talk.
The letter for the first sound of each word is missing.
Complete the words in the word frames below.

Find the correct letter
card, then copy the letter.

I can hear sounds in words and
write the letters for those sounds.

u

Say the word **upset**.
The word **upset** begins with the sound "**u**".

Where does this animal live? The word starts with the sound "**u**".
Say the word, then **colour** the picture.

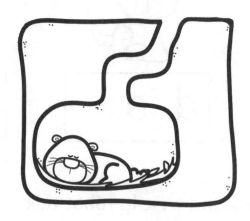

This is the letter for the sound "**u**".
Find all the arrows with this letter. **Circle** them.

k   p   u   u

u   o

u

u

The arrows point up. What
sound does **up** start with?

Trace over the grey letter with your finger.
Write over the dotted letters, then write some letters by yourself.

Start at the red dot.
Go down, curve round,
up, down and flick.

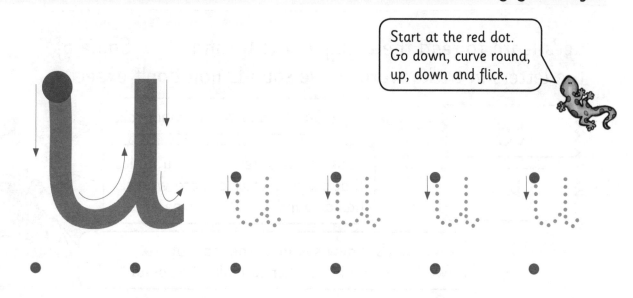

Look at the letter in the frame below. Say the sound.
Put a tick (✓) below the objects that start with this sound.

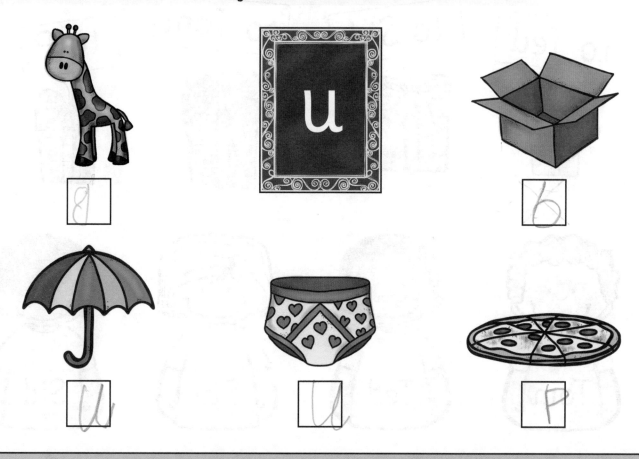

I can hear the sound "u". I can recognise
and write the letter for the sound "u".

Phonics — Reception Book 2

Tricky Words

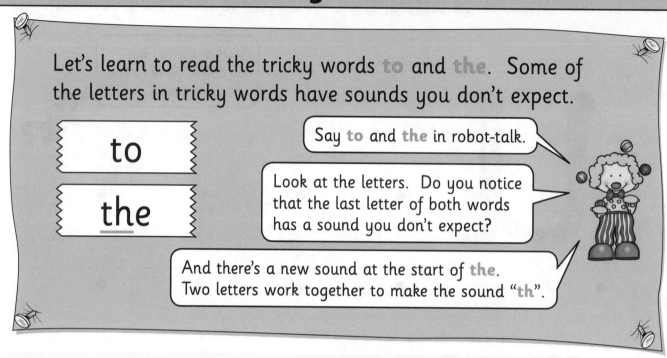

Let's learn to read the tricky words to and the. Some of the letters in tricky words have sounds you don't expect.

to

the

Say **to** and **the** in robot-talk.

Look at the letters. Do you notice that the last letter of both words has a sound you don't expect?

And there's a new sound at the start of **the**. Two letters work together to make the sound "**th**".

Read the labels on the presents. **Read** the children's names. **Draw** lines to give each child their present.

to Ted

to Sid

to Tom

to Pip

Tom

Ted

Pip

Sid

Did you remember? People's names always start with a capital letter. Why not colour the children's t-shirts the same colour as their presents?

Phonics — Reception Book 2

Read the captions. **Colour** the pictures.

You can't blend the sounds in tricky words — you just need to be able to read them straight away.

| in the sun |

| in the mud |

Read each caption. **Match** it to the correct picture.

| pin to the map |

| get to the top |

| kick to the net |

I can read captions with the words 'to' and 'the'.
I can remember that names start with capital letters.

r

Say the word **rose**.
What sound do you hear at the beginning?

Say what you see. All the words begin with the sound "**r**".
When you've said the words, **colour** the pictures.

This is the letter for the sound "**r**".
Find all the robots with this letter. **Circle** them.

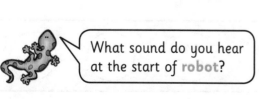
What sound do you hear
at the start of **robot**?

Trace over the grey letter with your finger.
Write over the dotted letters, then write some letters by yourself.

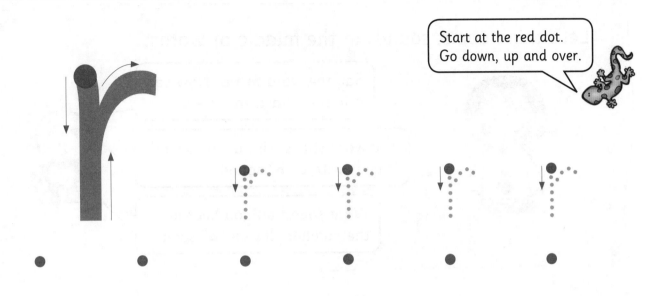

Start at the red dot.
Go down, up and over.

Look at the letter in the frame below. Say the sound.
Put a tick (✓) below the objects that start with this sound.

I can hear the sound "r". I can recognise
and write the letter for the sound "r".

Phonics — Reception Book 2

Practising Spelling

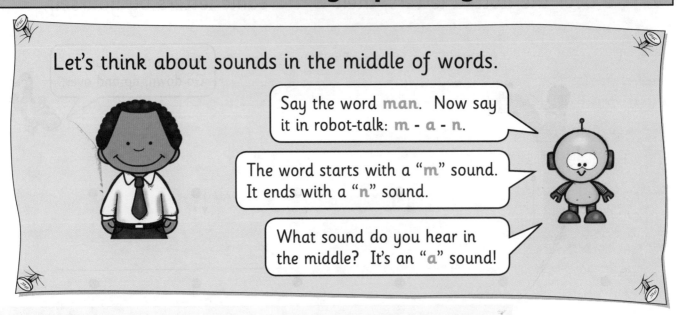

Let's think about sounds in the middle of words.

Say the word man. Now say it in robot-talk: m - a - n.

The word starts with a "m" sound. It ends with a "n" sound.

What sound do you hear in the middle? It's an "a" sound!

Say the word pet in robot-talk. What sound do you hear in the middle? Circle the correct letter card.

i   o   e

Say the words nut, tin and cot in robot-talk.
The letter for the middle sound of each word is missing. Write it.

Look at the letter cards. Find the card you need. Copy the letter.

o   u   i

| n | u | t |

| t | i | n |

| c | o | t |

Let's spell whole words now! You are going to say the word in robot-talk. Then you'll write a letter for each sound you say.

Say **mug** in robot-talk. **Write** the word in the word frame.

Find the letter card for each sound you say. Copy the letters into the word frame in the correct order.

mug

Say what you see, then **say** that word in robot-talk.
Write the words in the word frames using letters on the letter cards.

map   sun   peg

g   e   m   u   p

p   n   s   a

It's a good idea to cross out the letters as you use them.

I can spell words and write the letters in the correct order.

h

Say the word **hedgehog**.
The word **hedgehog** begins with the sound "**h**".

Say what you see. All the words begin with the sound "**h**".
When you've said the words, **colour** the pictures.

This is the letter for the sound "**h**".
Find all the hats with this letter. **Circle** them.

Say the sound the
word **hat** starts with.

Phonics — Reception Book 2

© CGP — Not to be photocopied

Trace over the grey letter with your finger.
Write over the dotted letters, then write some letters by yourself.

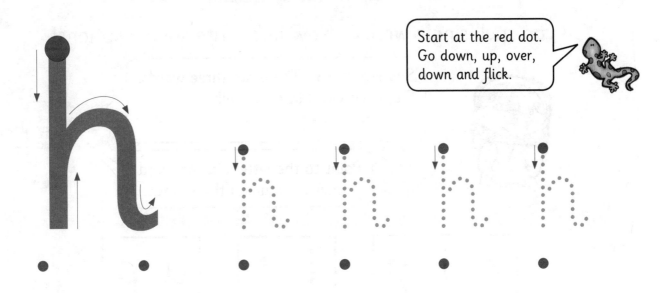

Start at the red dot.
Go down, up, over,
down and flick.

Look at the letter in the frame below. Say the sound.
Put a tick (✓) below the objects that start with this sound.

I can hear the sound "h". I can recognise
and write the letter for the sound "h".

Phonics — Reception Book 2

Writing Captions

You can spell single words. Now let's write some captions!

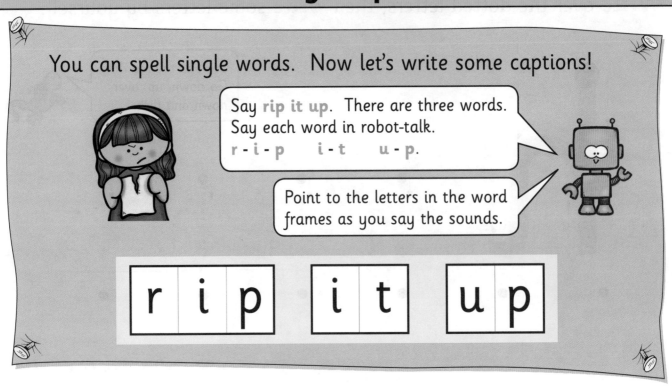

Say **rip it up**. There are three words. Say each word in robot-talk.
r - i - p   i - t   u - p.

Point to the letters in the word frames as you say the sounds.

| r | i | p | | i | t | | u | p |

Say **pin it on**, then **say** those words in robot-talk.
Point to the letters in the word frames as you say the sounds.
Copy the letters into the empty word frames below.

| p | i | n | | i | t | | o | n |

Each word has its own word frame.
Notice that there's a space between each word.

Where's the fish? It's **on a rod**. The last two words are missing.
Say the words in robot-talk. **Write** them into the word frames.

Find the letter card for each sound you say. Copy the letters into the word frame in the correct order.

| o | n | | a | | r | o | d |

d a o r

Where's the fish? It's **in a net**. All the words are missing!
Say the words in robot-talk. **Write** them into the word frames.

Cross out the letters as you use them.

| | | | | | h | e | t |

n t a n i e

I can spell words and write simple captions.

Phonics — Reception Book 2

b

Say the word **butterfly**.
Say the sound the word **butterfly** begins with.

Say what you see. All the words begin with the sound "**b**".
When you've said the words, **colour** the pictures.

This is the letter for the sound "**b**".
Find all the bags with this letter. **Circle** them.

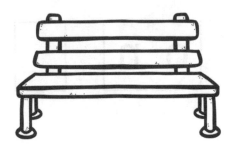

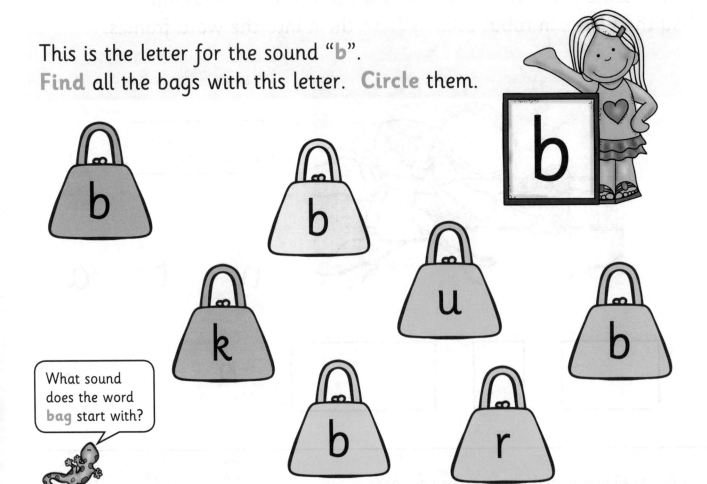

What sound
does the word
bag start with?

Trace over the grey letter with your finger.
Write over the dotted letters, then write some letters by yourself.

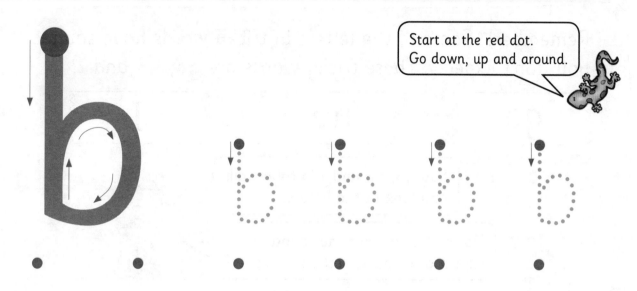

Start at the red dot.
Go down, up and around.

Look at the letter in the frame below. Say the sound.
Put a tick (✓) below the objects that start with this sound.

I can hear the sound "b". I can recognise
and write the letter for the sound "b".

More Tricky Words

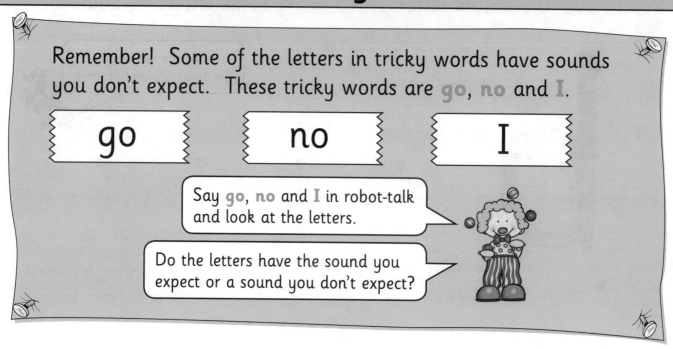

Remember! Some of the letters in tricky words have sounds you don't expect. These tricky words are go, no and I.

| go | no | I |

Say go, no and I in robot-talk and look at the letters.

Do the letters have the sound you expect or a sound you don't expect?

Read the captions. **Colour** the pictures.

go up   go in   go on

Look at the sign. **Read** the captions.
Circle the correct caption.

no hens

no dogs

Practise tricky words until you can read them straight away!

Look at each picture. Read the captions below.
Circle the best caption for that picture.

I hum	I cut	I dig
I hop	I run	I nod

Read each caption. Match it to the correct picture.

the kids go to a bus

no top on the red pen

Meg and I had a hug

 Did you remember the tricky words **the** and **to**?

I can read captions with the words 'go', 'no' and 'I', and remember the words 'the' and 'to'.

Phonics — Reception Book 2

f

Say the word fire.
Do you hear the sound "f" at the beginning?

Say what you see. All the words begin with the sound "f".
When you've said the words, colour the pictures.

This is the letter for the sound "f".
Find all the flags with this letter. Circle them.

f   f

f   o

m   r

f

The word flag starts
with the sound "f".

Trace over the grey letter with your finger.
Write over the dotted letters, then **write** some letters by yourself.

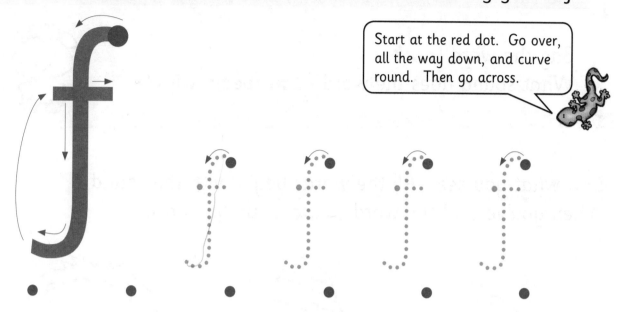

Start at the red dot. Go over, all the way down, and curve round. Then go across.

Look at the letter in the frame below. **Say** the sound.
Put a **tick** (✓) below the objects that start with this sound.

I can hear the sound "f". I can recognise and write the letter for the sound "f".

Phonics — Reception Book 2

l

Say the word **lamb**.
What sound does the word **lamb** begin with?

Say what you see. All the words begin with the sound "l".
When you've said the words, **colour** the pictures.

This is the letter for the sound "l".
Find all the lollipops with this letter. **Circle** them.

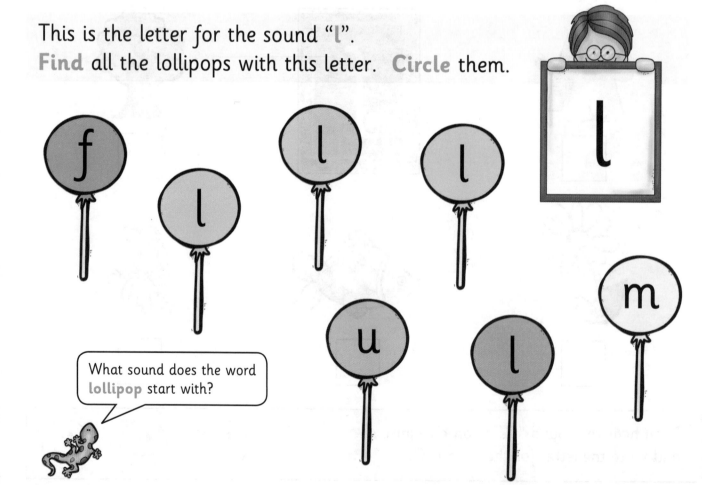

What sound does the word
lollipop start with?

Trace over the grey letter with your finger.
Write over the dotted letters, then **write** some letters by yourself.

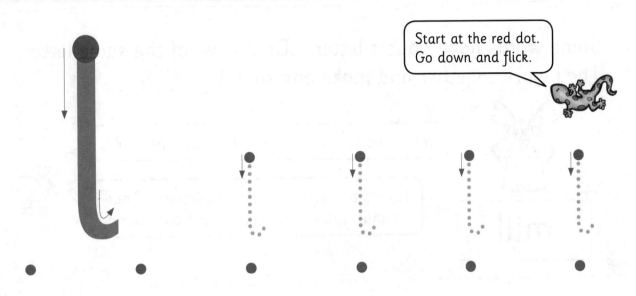

Start at the red dot.
Go down and flick.

Look at the letter in the frame below. **Say** the sound.
Put a **tick** (✓) below the objects that start with this sound.

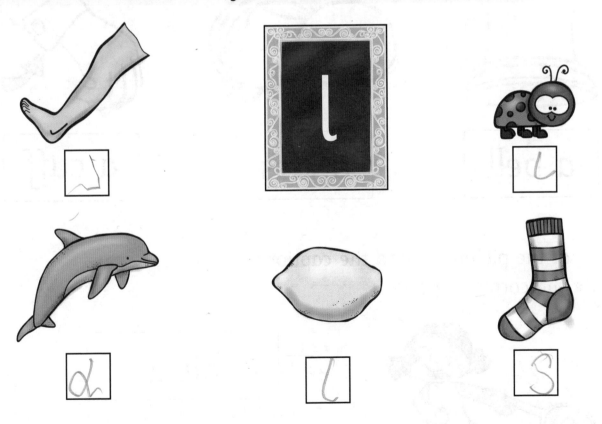

I can hear the sound "l". I can recognise
and write the letter for the sound "l".

Phonics — Reception Book 2

Double Letters

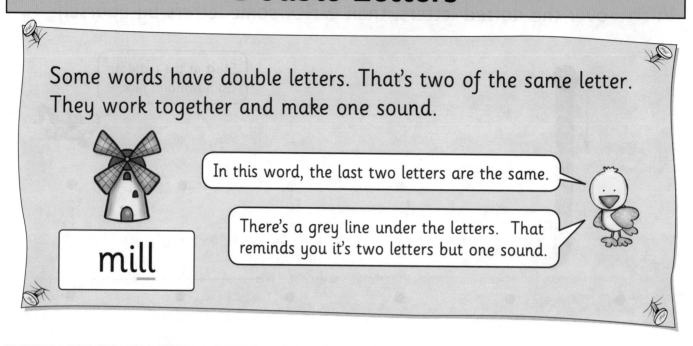

Some words have double letters. That's two of the same letter. They work together and make one sound.

In this word, the last two letters are the same.

There's a grey line under the letters. That reminds you it's two letters but one sound.

mill

Read the captions. **Colour** the pictures.

a bell

a kiss

a cuff

Look at the picture. **Read** the captions.
Circle the correct caption.

hit it

miss it

Read the caption. **Circle** the correct picture.

There's a story about a wolf who huffs and puffs. Do you know it?

| it can hu_f_f and pu_f_f |

Read each caption. **Match** it to the correct picture.

| on a hi_l_l |

| in a me_ss_ |

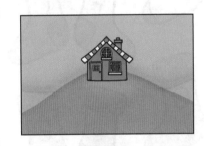

Read the caption. **Draw** a picture to go with the caption.

| a do_ll_ on a mat |

I know that when the same two letters are next to each other they make one sound.

Phonics — Reception Book 2

Capital Letters

The letter on this sock has the sound "b".

The letter on this sock has the sound "b" too! It looks different because it's a capital letter.

The letters on each pair of socks have the same sound.
Say the sounds. **Circle** the capital letters.

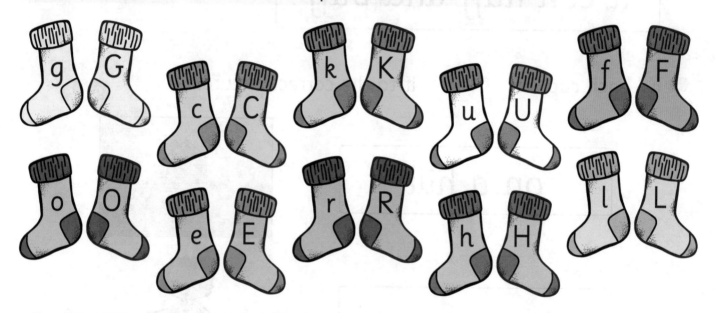

Draw lines to match each letter with its capital letter.
Colour both puzzle pieces the same colour.

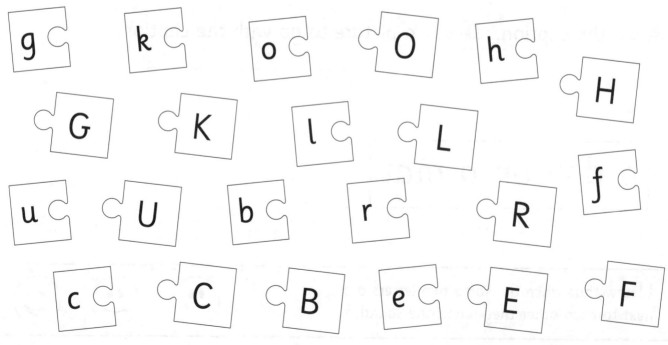

Draw over the dotted letters to write the capital letters.
Start at the red dot and follow the arrows.

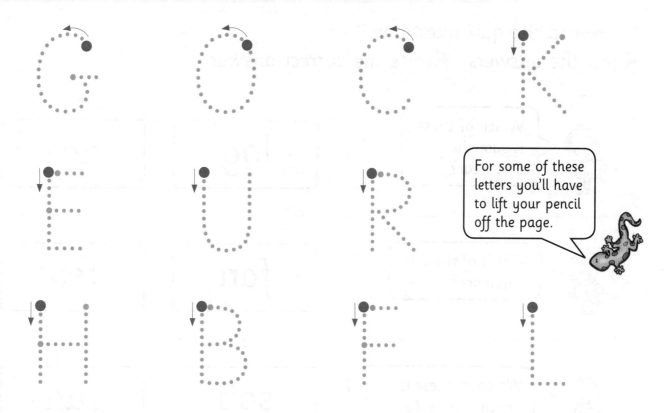

For some of these letters you'll have to lift your pencil off the page.

People's names start with a capital letter. So do pets' names!
Circle the names that are written correctly.

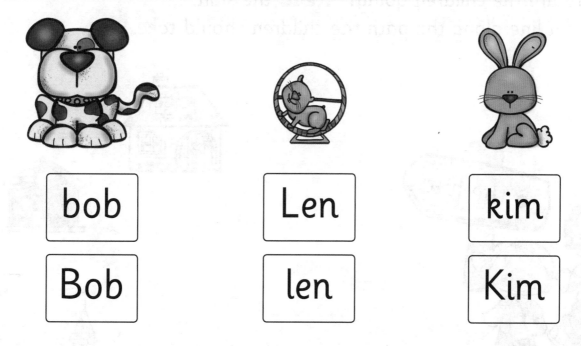

| bob | Len | kim |
| Bob | len | Kim |

I can recognise some more capital letters.
I remember that names start with capital letters.

Grand Finale

Listen to the quiz questions.
Read the answers. Circle the correct answer.

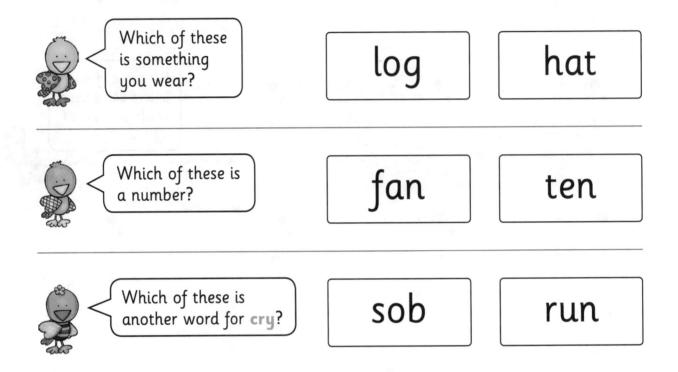

Which of these is something you wear?	log	hat
Which of these is a number?	fan	ten
Which of these is another word for cry?	sob	run

Where are the children going? Read the sign.
Draw a line along the path the children should take.

to the hut

Read the description. **Circle** the correct picture.

a big dog on a bed

All these words begin and end with the same letter.
Write the letter that is missing from the middle.

p i p

p o p

p u p

o

u

i

Colour the picture.
The letters on the crayons show you where to use each colour.

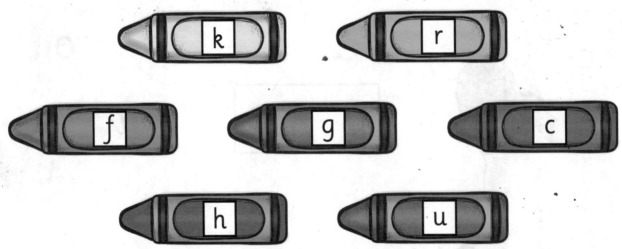

EROW211